THE EDGAR CAYCE *IDEALS* WORKBOOK

Taking Control of Your Life

by
Kevin Todeschi

THE EDGAR CAYCE *IDEALS* WORKBOOK

Taking Control of Your Life

by
Kevin Todeschi

A·R·E
PRESS

ASSOCIATION FOR
RESEARCH AND
ENLIGHTENMENT

Based on Concepts from the Edgar Cayce Material

A.R.E. Press • Virginia Beach • Virginia

ISBN 87604-259-0

4th Printing, June 1997

Printed in U.S.A

What your destiny is depends upon what you will do with yourself in relationship to your ideal.

Edgar Cayce
Twentieth-Century Mystic

Acknowledgments

A great deal of thanks are due to Mark Thurston, Kieth VonderOhe, and Shirley Winston. Without their suggestions, their reading and re-reading of the text, and their start-to-finish dedication, this workbook might never have become a reality.

Author's note: Many of the exercises contained in this workbook were suggested by the Edgar Cayce readings, or were based on suggestions contained in the readings. You will probably want to complete this workbook *in pencil*, allowing you to make changes and redo specific exercises at some point in the future.

TABLE OF CONTENTS

PREFACE

Why Do You Need a Guidebook to Chart Your Life's Path?

You might just as well ask, "Why would I want a map in order to drive somewhere I've never been before?" Most of you taking your first cross-country trip in an automobile would surely plan your course with care. Before leaving the house, you would do the preliminary work necessary to find the right roads, highways, and interstates on which you would need to travel. The map would be your guide for the simple reason that you wanted to reach your destination in the shortest and safest way possible. Only the most pioneering (or foolhardy) individuals would simply get into the car and, with no planning, try to make such a lengthy journey—all the time *hoping* to arrive.

Yet, it's this very same approach of just getting into a vehicle and starting out that most individuals use to travel the journey of life. You might have a sense that there's a purpose to your journey. Individuals who are truly lucky might even know what their purpose is. But for most, the trip itself becomes so demanding that there is little time to even ponder the destination.

This material has been compiled as a means of making the most of your journey ahead. You'll have the opportunity to contemplate the roads you're taking and the luggage you've brought along. Your guidebook will help you become the navigator of your life's destination rather than simply a sometimes-reluctant passenger. By reading the text and doing the exercises, you will:

• Have a clearer idea of where you are in your life right now and how it relates to where you would like to be.

• Understand the importance of your emotions and feelings, and the impact they have on every aspect of your experiences in life.

• Discover the kind of thinking that just might lead you in the direction you really desire to go.

• Have the tools necessary to start becoming the kind of person you want to be.

This guidebook contains self-assessment tools that will be useful for "taking the wheel" of your life's journey. It has been designed for you to go through at your own pace—you could finish many of the exercises in one day or over a period of weeks. When completed, you will have identified how you got to where you are, and you will have chosen the destination toward which you'd really like to be headed—a destination that might seem beyond your wildest possibilities.

This might sound like work, but it can be fun and it will certainly be worth the effort, for what could be more worthwhile than taking control of your life's direction.

STEP ONE: Finding Out Where You Are

Have you ever wondered how you got into certain situations in your life? Have you ever asked yourself, "What could happen next?" Have you ever felt lost?

Most of us get so caught up in the activities and frustrations of our lives that we forget our purpose for living. Yet, it's that very same purpose—even if it's unconscious—coupled with choices, choices (and more choices) that led us to our current life's experiences. It's the reason we find ourselves where we are right now. Therefore, one of the first steps to becoming the navigator of your life's journey is to become aware of what is currently motivating your life. This might simply be called "starting where you're at."

The results of this step could be that you'll find yourself satisfied with the central influence guiding your life. In that case, the next step will let you become aware of more effective ways to stay on track. On the other hand, from the exercises in Step One, you might discover that you're not totally satisfied with where your life has been taking you. If that happens, then you'll have every right to change your direction. You can take the wheel of your vehicle and turn toward a new destination.

What Excites You? What Makes You Happy? Where Is Your Joy?

One of the motivating influences in your life comes from the things that give you happiness and joy. By looking at who and what those things are, you'll gain a first glimpse of where you are in your life right now.

Exercise 1.1

What makes you enthusiastic and joyful about life? Is there an activity that causes you to become so absorbed that you momentarily lose touch with everything else? Is there something you enjoy doing so much that you forget all about the time?

For a few moments, close your eyes and think about situations or activities that create this feeling of enjoyment for you. When you've finished, write your answers here:

_____

_____

_____

_____

_____

_____

_____

_____

Next, try to recall any activities from childhood that gave you a similar feeling of total absorption. Were there things that you used to enjoy especially more than others? Perhaps you liked playing certain types of games, or being in a particular place, or doing specific things all alone, or simply spending time with special friends. For a few moments, close your eyes and think back to the time when you were a child.

List here the activities you enjoyed that come to mind:

_____

_____

_____

_____

_____

_____

Consider what you've written down in answering both questions, and see if any themes or patterns might already be evident. Is there anything that both of them have in common? For example, do your answers indicate that you have some of your happiest experiences when your journey involves other people? Do you simply enjoy being with others? Maybe you're a "people person," or perhaps you enjoy things that are competitive in nature?

On the other hand, do your answers indicate that one pattern that gives you the greatest joy is an activity done alone? Perhaps reading or just spending quiet time by yourself is one of your greatest joys.

Perhaps you'll see that your favorite activities involve mostly physical or mostly mental pursuits? Or maybe you enjoy a balance of both.

You may also see that the things that give you the greatest joy have changed as you matured—your enthusiastic, happy times come in different ways now than they used to.

If you can isolate an underlying theme or pattern that seems to give you the greatest happiness in your life right now, try wording it in a few sentences here: (for example, "spending time alone")

_____

_____

_____

_____

_____

_____

This theme is one central influence in your life. Consciously or unconsciously, it can be a powerful motivator. Everyone wants to be happy and joyful. Because you've had experiences of happiness due to this pattern before, you've learned that it's something to look for again.

Exercise 1.2

Using a similar approach, is there anything in your life right now that causes you frustration, pain, or unhappiness? Does something make you lose touch with the positive aspects of living?

For a few moments, close your eyes and think about situations or activities that create this feeling of frustration or pain. When you've finished, write your answers here:

_____

_____

_____

_____

Next, try to remember if there were any instances from your childhood that gave you a similar feeling. Are there things you can still recall that used to be painful or hard for you to deal with? Perhaps you often felt lonely, or maybe you spent a great amount of time wishing things were different for you. For a few moments, close your eyes and think back to the time when you were a child.

List anything you found painful or tried unsuccessfully to deal with:

_____

_____

_____

_____

Review what you've written to both questions, and see if any additional themes or patterns are evident. Just as in the above positive example, you may find that the frustrations and pain you experienced as a child remain with you even today. For example, maybe you've always had a hard time feeling love and affection, or perhaps a difficult relationship from the past remains difficult even now for one reason or another.

If you found an underlying painful pattern, write it here:

_____

_____

_____

_____

_____

_____

_____

You'll use the information from both Exercises 1.1 and 1.2 in the next exercise.

Exercise 1.3

Although the main purpose of this workbook is to help you chart your future course, sometimes looking back can be very helpful. It can be as important for you to know where you came from as it is to know where you are going. Why? There are at least two reasons: (1) Your *current* patterns in life may be a continuation of themes from the past—and it might be easier to see them by looking back; and (2) From your recollections of childhood you can sometimes catch hints of the very purpose for which you were born. In other words, each of us came into this life with a mission—a special purpose that may be evident from childhood interests and talents.

In terms of themes from the past, if you look carefully at your life—and your current situation—can you see patterns of behavior from your childhood that you're still relying on in the present? For example, if you frequently threw a temper tantrum in order to get what you wanted at age five, you may still be expressing this pent-up energy to get your way as an adult, even though your current method may be somewhat different. In other words, you may still be reacting to people and circumstances as if *your* way makes more sense than theirs. Or, as a more positive example, if you were always curious as a child, you may find that this innate impetus to explore and test the limits around you still motivates you. It may have propelled you into both wanted *and* unwanted situations in your adult life.

As you look back at your attitudes, tendencies, and behaviors as a child, which ones seem to have carried through into adulthood (even if their way of being expressed has changed)? List any you recognize here:

_____

_____

_____

Do any of these lifelong patterns help to explain why you've had recurring problems or frustrating situations?

_____

_____

_____

_____

Oftentimes, as a young child, you may have expressed interest in some favorite game or toy, or discussed what you wanted to be when you grew up. Looking at these memories now might actually provide inklings of your underlying *soul's purpose*. Do you remember any of these special interests or talents? Can any of these recollections suggest clues about your purpose?

_____

_____

_____

_____

_____

_____

_____

Exercise 1.4

Finding out where you are currently in the journey of life also means having an inspection—not the kind done once a year by your local service station, but one you do yourself as a review of how you use your time and your energy on a regular basis.

Think of a *typical* day (or week) in your life. Make a list of the activities (or thoughts) that seem to repeatedly occupy your waking hours. Some of the activities you note will be positive ones: for example, playing with your children, meditating daily, or doing regular exercise. Others may be less positive, such as doing another person's work over and over again at the office, constantly picking up after others, making certain that your boss is aware of all that you're doing, or "reacting" to constantly changing circumstances rather than "acting" out the events of your day.

Try to list about a dozen activities that occupy most of your time:

1._____

2._____

3._____

4._____

5._____

6._____

7._____

8._____

9._____

10._____

11._____

12._____

Now, review the list. Does something seem to occupy your time more than anything else? Can any of your activities, thoughts, or feelings be linked by a central theme? For example: Do you spend more time worrying about the needs of others rather than your own needs? Do you spend too much time making certain that everything you do will be appreciated? Do you constantly have to invest time and energy in order to justify your previous actions?

List one or two themes that the items in the above list may have in common:

_____

_____

_____

_____

_____

_____

Are there any items on your list which you would consider fear-based; that is, reactions caused by your own fears, insecurities or defense mechanisms? Put an "F" in the margin next to those items which occupy your time and are fear-centered.

Do you recognize any of these activities as joy-centered; things in which you invest regular amounts of time and energy that help to promote feelings of joy, enthusiasm, or happiness within yourself? Put a "J" in the margin next to these.

After you've "inspected" your typical day, you'll be ready to move on to the next exercise which deals with personal change.

Exercise 1.5

Is there anything you want to change most about yourself and your current situation in life? The motivation for personal change is often ambiguous. Because of your changing moods and attitudes, something that makes you happy one moment may be the cause of frustration the next. You may even have a personal behavior, habit, or attitude that is something you thoroughly enjoy *sometimes* but hope to change at *other times*.

One example might be your enjoyment of food versus your reoccurring desire to lose weight. Another example might be the enjoyment of relaxing with a cigarette in opposition to your desire to quit smoking. This kind of ambiguity can also relate to attitudes as well. For example, you might be torn between your love for personal freedom on the one hand and the never-ending commitments to your family on the other.

For most individuals, these paradoxical tensions are a regular part of life. By taking the time to examine them for yourself, you can begin to look more objectively at your own life. You're likely to see that these opposing desires are a key part of knowing where you are right now.

Is there anything in your life that could be considered "opposing desires"? For any of them can you see why the best part of yourself would support one side rather than another?

_____

_____

_____

_____

_____

_____

Now, looking at your answers to the above question *and* to the answers you've written for the previous exercises, try to get clear about *the most significant changes you'd like to make in your current life situation.* Be as objective and as loving as you can. The purpose of this exercise is not to make you feel guilty about your faults or to make you dissatisfied with situations that aren't going exactly right in your life. It's simply an attempt to recognize your current status in life and the places where you desire change. Make two columns: what you'd like to change about yourself and what you'd like to have changed in the situations and conditions around you.

DESIRED CHANGES IN ME	DESIRED CHANGES AROUND ME
Example:	
To have greater self-confidence	*I wish that people would listen more to my opinions*

The chart that you've just filled out is the single most important part to "Step One: Finding Out Where You Are." You've had the opportunity to look at your past, as well as to examine some current conditions in your life. Some of what you've seen probably pleases you, but other conditions may involve changes that you'd like to make.

How can you implement those changes? The secret rests with ideals and motives. In fact, the steps that follow in this workbook will help you plot your course for making those changes—not only altering those things you don't like, but also taking the initiative to head toward conditions that you do.

But before taking your next step, let's consider what "motivation" actually means and how closely it's related to ideals and purposes. Two examples make this point:

Example A:

There were two neighbors living side by side in the suburbs. Recently, both had obtained a labrador puppy. The first neighbor, we'll call him "Jack," was delighted with his new dog. He and his wife had always wanted a pet, and they were both excited about the addition of the puppy to their family. The second neighbor, we'll call him "Ed," couldn't stand dogs—hated them in fact—but he had finally relented to his children's continued request. Since both Ed and Jack now had dogs, each of them went to the hardware store and obtained identical "doghouse kits." They had the same task: to build a new house for a puppy.

The whole time Jack was building his doghouse he thought about how excited he was to have a pet ("man's best friend"), how much the puppy would like his new home, how the dog would be kept warm in the doghouse all year round, etc. However, the whole time Ed was building his house he was filled with thoughts of anger and disgust: Why had he ever given in to his children's request? He hurriedly constructed the doghouse, thinking that at least it would keep that "dirty dog" outside and out of his way.

When the doghouses are completed, even though they might appear identical, they won't be. Every time Jack looks at the doghouse, his experience will be entirely different from Ed's. His motivation was affirmative, and therefore his perception about the doghouse will always be more positive. Jack's motivating force was one of love; Ed's was one of anger.

Example B:

The movie *Chariots of Fire* demonstrates how people can have the same goal but have different motives, that is, different ideals for reaching that goal. Having different ideals means that the persons they are becoming, the persons they are "creating" themselves to be, is different. As the movie focuses on the lives of young men training for the 1924 Olympics, we learn about four of them who will represent Great Britain.

One young man, after having trained for many years, was finally on the boat traveling to France for the games. He wrote a letter home, and in the process asked himself the question, "Why am I doing this?" His answer was, "I am doing this for my family and my country." You might say that this man's "ideal" was loyalty. He had received so much from his family and his country that he wanted to repay them.

The second man was a member of the nobility. When he was asked why he spent so much time training, he responded, "For me, the whole thing is fun. Cast your cares aside ..." One of his ideals in life was to have fun. Running was one of the ways in which he lived out that ideal.

The third man was Jewish. Though he had money, because of his ethnic background he always felt that he had to prove himself equal to other Englishmen. Just before the final 100 meter race for the gold, the third man said, "I am here to justify my existence." His ideal was to prove that he was as good as anyone else. Winning the Olympic gold medal was one way to do that.

The fourth man came from a missionary family and was training to go to China. In addition to possessing the desire to lead a religious life, however, he also had the gift of speed. When his sister became concerned that his Olympic training was distracting him from his true calling, he responded, "God made me for a purpose—China. God also made me fast. When I run I feel God's pleasure. To give it up is to hold God in contempt. It's not just fun. To run is to honor God."

These four men all had the same goal—winning Olympic gold medals. However, each of them had different ideals that motivated them as they worked toward the goal: being loyal to family and country, having fun, proving oneself equal to others, and honoring God. Although observers might not be able to see how ideals influenced these four men, each of them was building a different life because of the ideals that he held.

These two examples suggest that you have motives or "ideals" for doing what you do, even though you may not be particularly conscious of them. In fact, the strongest motivating forces in your life *right now* are your current ideals.

This is the other half of the answer to the focus for "Step One: Finding Out Where You Are." You've already identified aspects of your life that you'd like to change. Now let's identify the ideals that currently shape your life. The following exercises will help you see what the current ideals are in your life.

Exercise 1.6

Choices, choices, and more choices. Life is full of decisions—most of them minor, but some of them life-changing.

Can you remember a time when you made a major decision that affected you profoundly? Perhaps it was a new job opportunity that took you to another city? Perhaps it was marriage or even a divorce? Perhaps it was a risky venture?

Let's look at a series of decisions you've made and then look for any clues they may offer about your current ideals. Try to pick five big decisions you've made recently. (Make sure you select situations where *you* were the decision-maker, rather than events where a change or a decision was forced upon you.) Try to select decisions that covered a variety of areas in your life: relationships, career, financial, or even leisure time.

What was the decision?

Decision #1: _____

Decision #2: _____

Decision #3: _____

Decision #4: _____

Decision #5: _____

What criterion did you use to make each decision (e.g., "I needed more money")?

Decision #1: _____

Decision #2: _____

Decision #3: _____

Decision #4: _____

Decision #5: _____

What steps did you take to evaluate your final choice (e.g., "I listed all the pros and cons")?

Decision #1: _____

Decision #2: _____

Decision #3: _____

Decision #4: _____

Decision #5: _____

For each of the five decisions, list other options that were available to you—alternatives you could have chosen but decided against:

For #1:_____

For #2:_____

For #3:_____

For #4:_____

For #5:_____

Review the notes you've made about these five decisions. Do you see any recurrent themes (for example, "I always choose the least complicated path" or "I always choose what I think someone else wants me to do"). What do the final decisions that you made tell you about yourself?

_____

_____

_____

_____

_____

_____

_____

From what you can observe in these decisions, what would you say is your central ideal (or "ideals," if you've identified more than one motive that alternately influences your life)?

_____

_____

_____

_____

_____

Exercise 1.7

We can often find clues to our own nature, our qualities, and our personality by looking at people we have known in life and examining our reactions to them (positive or negative). You might call these individuals "sign-posts along the way."

First, the positive:

In the following space, write the name of the person (living or deceased) whom you particularly admire or love (a person who stood out more than the others in your life):

_____

Close your eyes for just a moment and try to imagine this person standing before you. Think about his or her qualities, talents, and traits. Then list those qualities in the left-hand column. For each quality, try to decide exactly what it is about that characteristic that appeals to you, making notes in the right-hand column:

QUALITY	ADMIRABLE BECAUSE
Example:	
Outgoing personality	*She makes me feel comfortable around her*

Now, the negative:

In the following space, please write the name of a person (living or deceased) who causes you the greatest amount of frustration or even anger:

_____

Close your eyes for just a moment and try to imagine this second person standing before you. What is it about him or her that causes you to feel anger? Now list those traits in the left-hand column, and try to decide exactly what it is about that trait that makes you feel the way you do:

TRAIT	IRRITATING BECAUSE
Example:	
Extremely egotistical	*He constantly has "the answer" for everything*
_____	_____
_____	_____
_____	_____
_____	_____
_____	_____
_____	_____

Surprisingly, it is from these two lists (a positive person and a negative one) that you'll be able to discover a great deal about your own life's journey. If you can discern some of the influences that might be motivating these two individuals' lives, you'll see occasions when you appear to be traveling down the same highway. For example, there is a saying that "like attracts like." You're basically unable to have an *intense emotional reaction* (positive or negative) to a trait or a quality unless that very same trait or quality is a reflection of something in yourself. Perhaps those qualities are somewhat dormant in you, and maybe you haven't developed them to the same extent, or perhaps those faults don't appear as blatant in you as they do in the other person. But if you see something in another person that you have an *intense emotional reaction to*, and this same trait doesn't affect others in the same manner it affects you [for example, most individuals react negatively to a person who treats others cruelly], you can feel fairly certain that it's part of your own make-up (even if the way it manifests in you is different from the way the person does it).

Pick the one or two qualities/talents from the above "positive" person that you would most like to have in yourself:

_____

_____

_____

Pick the one or two traits/faults from the above "negative" person that you would least like to have as part of yourself:

_____

_____

_____

A Look in the Rear-View Mirror

Each of you must choose your own ideals and directions; it won't work if someone else chooses them for you. Only you can decide where you are right now and where you really should be going. Why? Here is an analogy: Suppose you received a call from someone who asked for directions to Washington, D.C. Would you be able to help that individual? You couldn't unless you knew where the person was calling from. Although the destination might be the same, the route would be different for someone calling from Philadelphia than it would be for someone calling from New York City. Everyone must refer to his or her own personalized road map for the journey through life, because each individual is the only person who can decide who they are, where they're headed, and what they wish they were doing.

In this first step you've had a chance to see more clearly where you are now in life—that is, "where you're calling from." You've seen patterns that mold your daily experience, some of them with an origin in your childhood. You've identified aspects of yourself and your situation that you'd like to change. And you've caught a glimpse of the central motives that shape your life's journey.

To conclude this step, try the following exercise. It's been found that "sentence completion" (filling in your first response to a suggested series of words) can be invaluable at providing objective answers and insights into your own life.

If I could change any pattern (or motivation) that has been operating in my life, it would be to

_____

_____

I think that the one quality I like best about myself is my ability to

_____

_____

And, we'll proceed down the road . . .

STEP TWO:
Deciding Where You Want to Go

Having explored where you are, the next logical step is to make a decision about your direction. Where do you want to go next?

It might surprise you to learn that you have always been motivated by your ideals, whether it was done consciously or it just happened without your even thinking about it. In fact, these ideals have been responsible for the way you've handled every experience in your life. By making the decision to set your ideal *consciously*, you will be giving yourself a completely new approach to every aspect of your life. It will be like finding your own North Star.

In the past, even without modern-day equipment, sailors at sea could always tell exactly where they were. On a clear night, with an instrument called a sexton, they could "shoot the North Star," establish their bearing, and make certain that they were headed in the right direction. In this same manner, after having established your bearing in Step One, you can now choose your own North Star, your conscious ideal. Step Two will help you pick this North Star and thereby establish your own road map for your current journey through life. Once you have your personal road map, your direction will be more obvious.

Exercise 2.1

Your North Star, or ideal, may be thought of as a spiritual quality that you would like to have incorporated into all your daily activities. You will choose one word or a phrase that represents, for you, how you want to begin *acting* (as opposed to reacting) toward every individual and circumstance in your life right now.

To make it easier, close your eyes for a few moments and imagine a "perfect relationship." It could be a romantic involvement, a close friendship, or a meaningful relationship with even a wise or a holy individual. Think of it as one of the most positive relationships you could ever have with another person. Perhaps it's the same person you admire from Exercise 1.7, or it could be a very positive relationship in your life right now, or it might be a relationship that you've always imagined but haven't yet experienced. After you've imagined this relationship for a few minutes, then attempt to answer the following questions: [Caution: Don't begin this exercise until you've actually imagined the person and this relationship in your mind.]

Who is this person (or write "imaginary")?

_____

In this perfect relationship, how much time do you spend with one another?

_____

_____

_____

_____

_____

Is there a "common goal" toward which the two of you are working? If so, what is it?

_____

_____

_____

_____

_____

What interests do you have in common? For example, do you share spiritual interests, such as meditating or going to religious services? Mental pursuits, such as reading, paying bills, or just "making plans" together? Physical activities, such as gardening, traveling, or just "being together"?

Spiritual interests:_____

_____

_____

Mental pursuits: _____

_____

_____

Physical activities: _____

_____

_____

Is this perfect relationship one of "equals" or does one individual rely more heavily upon the other (it could be for advice, for comfort, or because one needs a "listening ear" more frequently)?

_____

_____

_____

_____

_____

_____

The purpose of this exercise is to assist you in becoming more objectively aware of the things you appreciate about "good" relationships. By so doing, the direction you'd like to take personally in terms of your interactions with others will become more obvious.

After reviewing your answers, use the following key and decide how important to you are each of the suggested qualities in this perfect relationship. In other words, try to scale the significance of each of the following one-word characteristics that make you feel really positive about this relationship. (IMPORTANT: Try to choose the two or three most important qualities, and then the two or three next most important ones. You won't want to give everything a "5" or a "4" simply to finish the exercise; seriously consider the qualities that are *most important to you.*)

5 = Extremely Important
4 = Somewhat Important
3 = Undecided/Indifferent
2 = Not Very Important
1 = Would Rarely Be Important

	5	4	3	2	1
1. LOVE	5	4	3	2	1
2. KINDNESS	5	4	3	2	1
3. JOY	5	4	3	2	1
4. UNDERSTANDING	5	4	3	2	1
5. PATIENCE	5	4	3	2	1
6. GENTLENESS	5	4	3	2	1
7. COMPASSION	5	4	3	2	1
8. FORGIVENESS	5	4	3	2	1
9. HUMOR	5	4	3	2	1
10. FAITH	5	4	3	2	1
11. TRUST	5	4	3	2	1
12. COMMITMENT	5	4	3	2	1
13. HOPE	5	4	3	2	1
14. OTHER: _____	5	4	3	2	1

When you've finished this exercise, list your four highest rated answers here:

1) _____

2) _____

3) _____

4) _____

From this exercise you've discovered some of the attributes and qualities that are important to you. Each of these characteristics can be invaluable for deciding "where you want to go," which is an essential purpose of Step Two and will be discussed in greater detail in Exercise 2.3.

However, another purpose of Step Two is to become aware of how often you may be "reacting to" individuals and circumstances in your life, instead of the more optimal approach of "acting on" each situation or condition as it arises. This ability becomes easier when you have a conscious "road map" (a conscious ideal) to help guide you.

The Purpose of a North Star in Daily Life

Have you ever had the experience of driving along "minding your own business," perhaps on your way to work or on your way home, when suddenly another vehicle pulls out in front of you, or cuts you off, or seems oblivious to the fact that it almost hit you? Invariably after this experience, your attitude and frame of mind, maybe even your blood pressure, were very different than they were before the encounter. *You might even say that you had a "reactionary response" to an external event that caused internal changes that you could even feel in your own mind and body.* It was a response that occurred automatically, without your even thinking about it.

In a similar manner, in our personal experiences and relationships with other people, we may often find ourselves behaving with a similar reactionary response. Many of our encounters, positive or negative, with the people with whom we're most familiar are almost automatic.

For example, have you ever been busy reading a paper, or sitting at your desk, or having your mind on something when suddenly someone else walked into the room? If you have a great deal of affection for this person, you might suddenly feel good (or happy) all over without knowing why, or your forehead might begin to grow warm, or you feel your heart suddenly "leap into your chest" . . . just by looking at another person. And the person may not have necessarily done anything to deserve such a positive response—at least not that day. When this has happened to you, it was a "reactionary response," perhaps based on previous encounters you've had with the person. Even though your response was positive, it occurred without consciously thinking about it.

On the other hand, have you ever had a less than positive "reactionary response" to another person? For example, when someone began walking toward you or perhaps simply came into your sight, have you ever begun to feel uneasy? Did the room suddenly "close in" around you? Did you immediately feel unhappy or angry just by looking at another person? Maybe the person hadn't necessarily done anything that day, but because of your past experiences with the individual you've "created" an automatic response to him or her. It happens without your even thinking about it and can affect your mood, perhaps even your entire day. In fact, at times your reactionary responses may seem to have greater control over your behavior than you do.

The purpose of this next exercise is to help you establish practical steps to begin "acting on" a problem relationship you may be experiencing rather than "reacting toward." This is another important factor for deciding where it is you want to go in your journey through life.

Exercise 2.2

Choosing a *conscious* road map or ideal is like making an intentional choice of direction. It is also like selecting your destination as it relates to *specific* circumstances or people. Because of reactionary responses, you've essentially created a "map" or a guidebook of your behavior as it relates to every individual, circumstance, and condition in your life. Making the conscious choice of your ideal will give you the awareness to decide objectively whether the course you've followed in the past is the same direction you wish to continue following or whether the time has come to look at a new map.

For this exercise, choose a "problem relationship" in your life. This person will be someone with whom you probably don't always get along. Perhaps this is an individual you've tried to work with before, but with little success. Or, it might be a person with whom you've had a problem for a long time but never actually tried to solve. He or she could be a family member, a neighbor, or a co-worker. This person may be someone who makes you feel uncomfortable, perhaps even "drives you crazy." The purpose of this exercise, however, is for you to pick someone with whom you'd like to improve your current relationship.

When you've decided, write that "problem relationship" person's name (or initials) here:

_____

There are four steps to this exercise. They are as follows:

1. First use three columns; in the first column, write the name of the person with whom you're having difficulties (e.g., "Larry").

2. In the second column, write the positive nature of the relationship that you would like to have with this person if your current reactionary response could somehow be transformed (e.g., "I'd like to be his friend").

3. In the third column, list all the ways this "new relationship" would make you feel.

4. When you've completed the first three columns, you're ready for column four. As you may remember from Step One, one of the most meaningful methods of working with relationships has to do with the concept of "like attracts like." This same concept will also be helpful in deciding what direction you need to take in solving a problem relationship. The last part of this exercise has to do with thinking of all the activities you can do in order to give the "feelings" you've listed in column three *to the person* with whom you'd like to improve your relationship. In column four list activities that correspond to the feelings you've listed in column three. (You might have more "activities" in column four than you've got "feelings" in column three, but try to have at least one activity in column four for every entry you've listed in three.)

Example:

Column One	Column Two	Column Three	Column Four
PERSON WITH WHOM YOU'RE HAVING DIFFICULTIES:	**DESIRED RELATIONSHIP:**	**WAYS THIS WOULD MAKE YOU FEEL:**	**ACTIVITY TO GIVE THIS RELATIONSHIP:**
Larry at work	*I want to be his friend*	*More comfortable in my working environment*	*Do everything I can do to make him feel comfortable around me*
		Happier to go to my job in the first place	*Being happy can be contagious; try to share this joy with him*
		More like "team" players instead of rivals	*Become cooperative with Larry, a real "team player"*
		Less suspicious of him "trying to get me"	*Trust Larry*
		More open to him when he was around, etc.	*Become a friend, etc.*

PERSON WITH WHOM YOU'RE HAVING DIFFICULTIES:	DESIRED RELATIONSHIP:
_____	_____
_____	_____
_____	_____
_____	_____
_____	_____
_____	_____
_____	_____
_____	_____
_____	_____
_____	_____
_____	_____
_____	_____

WAYS THIS WOULD MAKE YOU FEEL:	ACTIVITY TO GIVE THIS RELATIONSHIP
_____	_____
_____	_____
_____	_____
_____	_____
_____	_____
_____	_____
_____	_____
_____	_____
_____	_____
_____	_____
_____	_____
_____	_____
_____	_____

Certainly you don't want to become completely naive or foolish when you're trying to rebuild a relationship. For example, if you knew that Larry was a pathological liar, suddenly giving him complete and unbiased trust might be inappropriate; however, you can begin to trust that Larry is doing the best that he can and cultivate confidence between the two of you.

This exercise is helpful because it will let you become aware of a list of simple activities you can begin doing immediately to try to improve any difficult relationship. Even if there's a person you "like least of all in the entire world," you can begin to transform that relationship. To a great extent the transformation occurs within your own perception, but as you begin to see people differently, they will become different. Why? Because "like attracts like."

A simple way to begin is to try to minimize an individual's faults and to magnify the virtues. "Impossible!" you may say? Here is another way of looking at it:

"Even my best friend probably has someone who doesn't like him (or her) . . . and even my worst enemy probably has a best friend."

It's simply a matter of looking at a problem relationship in a different way than you've been used to, trying to overcome the reactionary responses and beginning to cultivate the relationship you'd like to have by attempting to give it to the person first. It will be like finding new friends along old highways.

In the same way that you've created a "map" which contains your new direction in terms of a specific problem relationship, you can create a conscious road map of any circumstance or situation. And you'll be able to use it for every area of your life, problems as well as opportunities. Making this road map is the essential purpose of Step Two because with it you'll be able to decide where you want to go, as well as how you're going to get there.

Exercise 2.3

Think of your ideal as a positive quality or a "spiritual example" that you would like to have reflected in all your activities, relationships, and decisions. The best way to begin is by choosing one word or phrase, which for you represents the *spirit* in which you would like to live your life right now. Choosing and then applying a spiritual ideal are the first major steps toward reorienting your life's direction and the motivational influences that have been "controlling" your life. An ideal is not a goal. It is the standard you will use to evaluate your goals and directions, and your reasons for pursuing those goals. The goal is what; the ideal is why!

Perhaps one of the simplest ways to begin is to pick one of the most important qualities you selected in Exercise 2.1, or you can pick an entirely different quality that you would consider a truly positive attribute. But your choice should be something that you'd like to have as part of your personal makeup, reflected in all of your activities; some quality or trait that you would like to achieve in your relationships with all other individuals—even those with whom you don't feel comfortable or those you don't like being around just yet.

For example, if you've had a difficult time with "forgiveness" in relationships, then perhaps that is the very quality on which you would begin working; if "compassion" is something you'd like to have reflected in your life's activities, then you may wish to pick it as your "road map"; perhaps "love" is the word that best expresses the ideal with which you'd like to begin working—whatever the word is right now, pick it. Don't worry about choosing a "final" ideal. Ideals grow and change as you do.

When you've decided what that quality or example is, write your word or phrase here:

_____

41

The following exercise is the "columned approach to ideals." It's similar to the previous exercise, but leaves room to include situations from every aspect of your current life. As before, you will work with four columns, but this time the columns are labeled differently:

1) At the top of the first column are the words "Situation/Person."

2) The second column is "My Spiritual Ideal"—the quality you wish to reflect in your life.

3) The third column is "My Mental Attitudes"—the mental thoughts or feelings you will need to hold in mind in order to bring your spiritual ideal into focus.

4) The fourth column is "My Physical Activities"—the physical things you can do that correspond to the new attitudes you'll be holding in mind.

Most individuals are involved in at least four areas in life: home, work, personal welfare (i.e., health and personal growth), and community (or other groups). Each of these areas will be affected by your personal road map. Eventually, you will need to work with each of them, one at a time; but for your first time, choose a specific individual, such as your spouse or a friend. You don't have to choose a "problem relationship" to work with first (although you can if you wish); you can decide to choose a person who is simply an important part of your life. Read through the entire example before trying to fill out your own columns.

For the example, we've chosen "spouse" as the person we're putting on the map. As an example of a spiritual ideal, we've chosen "love":

Example:

Column One (One word or phrase)	Column Two (One word or phrase)	Column Three (List)	Column Four (List each activity as corresponding to its respective attitude)
SITUATION PERSON	**MY SPIRITUAL IDEAL**	**MY MENTAL ATTITUDES**	**MY PHYSICAL ACTIVITIES**
My Spouse	*Love*	*Compassion*	*Listen with undivided attention when she speaks; become more aware of when she "needs" a listening ear*
		Responsibility	*"Take care of her" just as she takes care of me; do my best to give her what she needs*
		Respect	*She's a central part of my life; treat her always with this in mind—opening the door for her or walking side by side instead of way ahead*
		Forgiveness	*When I argue, make an effort to be the first to ask for forgiveness; forgive her just as I would want her to forgive me, and also forgive myself for becoming angry in the first place*
		Companionship	*Let us act as a "couple" instead of as two individuals; make joint decisions; do more things together; set aside "we" time*
		Joy	*Share my joy, not just my problems, with her; explore activities that we both like*

SITUATION/PERSON	MY SPIRITUAL IDEAL

MY MENTAL ATTITUDES	MY PHYSICAL ACTIVITIES
_____	_____
_____	_____
_____	_____
_____	_____
_____	_____
_____	_____
_____	_____
_____	_____
_____	_____
_____	_____
_____	_____
_____	_____
_____	_____

From the example you can see how the columns might be defined as follows:

Essentially, your *spiritual ideal* is a concept that indicates to you a more positive direction (or the most positive direction) that your life could be following. It's a spirit of living that is relevant and needed for *every* situation and relationship you face.

Your mental ideals or attitudes are different levels of awareness that you're trying to cultivate. They will relate to specific aspects of your life, how your thoughts are spent in recreation, study, work, social activities—everything you do with them!—because they're more than just a simple state of mind. They're cultivated by what you read, what you watch on TV, what you decide to know about, other certain choices you make. They're attitudes with such characteristics as forgiveness, joy, happiness, concern, expectation, and hope. In a sense, your mental ideals/attitudes can be identified by answering this question: "What attitude(s) should I hold in mind toward this part of my life so as to awaken a sense or a feeling of my spiritual ideal?" This attitude (or attitudes) should always be related to a particular aspect of your life.

Your physical ideals or activities are what you can do to bring the spiritual and mental ideals into the material world. They work in practical ways. They will be courses of action you can begin to take; for example, helping a co-worker with a project, visiting someone sick, praying for a person who needs direction, picking up the phone and making a call, helping someone with yardwork, inviting a lonely relative or friend to a meal, etc.

You may have noticed that column two, "my spiritual ideal," will remain the same for each area of your life, but columns three and four might be quite different.

For example, let's assume that your spiritual ideal is "understanding." Column three for "home" might include the following: "Try to maintain an attitude of family unity and togetherness even though we're all different individuals," "Cultivate a joyful attitude around Bill and the kids," "Approach tasks that need to be done in a good mood rather than with a sense of dread." Column three for "work" could include: "Cultivate an attitude of cooperation in the office," "Respect other approaches," "Appreciate what others contribute."

Column four, corresponding to "home" and "work" above, might appear as follows:

Home: "Plan a weekly family activity or gathering that we can all take part in," "Give the kids my *undivided* attention when they need to talk—or at homework time," "Set aside 'us time' for Bill and myself (and 'me time'—even for 10 minutes)," "Begin to cultivate teamwork for household chores."

Work: "Schedule a regular staff meeting with no other agenda than having everyone update everybody else as to what projects he or she is currently working on," "Don't be so quick to turn down a new approach just because we haven't done it that way before," "Say 'thank you' or 'well done' more often—don't just think it, say it!"

Now it's time to fill in your own road map or ideals chart. Begin with one area or person in your life, and when you've finished with that one expand your chart to include the others. Take your time. To do this exercise thoroughly will take you at least a half-hour to forty-five minutes or more. It will be well worth the time invested, however, because it is *your personal road map to life.* (You can refer to the example if you need help deciding which items go in what list.)

Example:			
Column One (One word or phrase)	Column Two (One word or phrase)	Column Three (List)	Column Four (List each activity as it corresponds to its respective attitude)
SITUATION/ PERSON	**MY SPIRITUAL IDEAL**	**MY MENTAL ATTITUDES**	**MY PHYSICAL ACTIVITIES**
Home (or specific person)			
Work (or specific person)			
Personal Welfare Groups, etc.			

SITUATION/PERSON	MY SPIRITUAL IDEAL
_____	_____
_____	_____
_____	_____
_____	_____
_____	_____
_____	_____
_____	_____
_____	_____
_____	_____
_____	_____
_____	_____
_____	_____
_____	_____

MY MENTAL ATTITUDES	MY PHYSICAL ACTIVITIES
_____	_____
_____	_____
_____	_____
_____	_____
_____	_____
_____	_____
_____	_____
_____	_____
_____	_____
_____	_____
_____	_____
_____	_____
_____	_____

After completing this exercise for one specific person in your life, expand your road map to encompass all other areas of your life (home, work, personal welfare, and other groups). You'll be referring to this chart throughout the remainder of your Ideals Workbook.

You now have a list of practical things you can begin thinking about and doing in every area of your life as a way of heading toward your spiritual ideal. As you begin seeing some progress—some movement along your road—you may discover additional physical activities and mental attitudes that you can incorporate into a specific relationship at home or at work. Add these activities/attitudes to your chart. As you make progress, you may also decide to re-evaluate your current ideal, choosing something more "difficult" or more specific to current events in your life. Remember, your ideals grow and change as you do. The point is to first choose and then to apply a spiritual ideal to your life.

So far in Step Two you've established a list of spiritual qualities that you think are important in relationships with other people. You've also chosen for yourself a quality that you would like to begin working with in your own life, and you've seen how to begin working with a problem relationship with the "like attracts like" concept. The culmination of these exercises was the establishment of your own personal road map which you will be working with and fine-tuning throughout the rest of this workbook.

Now that you've established your direction (your spiritual ideal) and formulated your road map, this next exercise will demonstrate how you can use your ideal to make decisions. Column four in the last two exercises showed you some of the "how am I going to get there?" aspects of ideals once you've established a direction for yourself. Learning how to make decisions with ideals is simply another.

Making Decisions with Your Road Map

One of the most effective ways of "taking the wheel" in your life is to begin making decisions based on your work with ideals and self-observation. This is one way that using your personal road map can become practical. In fact, this method of decision making can often make your life seem a lot less complicated and decisions will be arrived at more easily. The following example will illustrate:

A woman in her early twenties had recently graduated from college, though she still lived at home. Let's call her Jennifer. She had found a good job and wanted to get an apartment of her own. Her parents, however, were against the idea. They suggested that she wait until she was more settled in her new job and they gave her every imaginable reason why it just wouldn't be a good idea right now—but she knew that the real reason was because she would be missed. Jennifer was an only child, and they would feel lost without her. Her parents realized that her moving out was inevitable, but they felt she could wait a little while longer.

Jennifer was totally confused. On the one hand she felt as if it was time for her to be on her own, and on the other hand she loved her parents and didn't want to hurt them. She was torn between staying for one more year and being out on her own.

So, in this example, how can working with ideals help Jennifer to make a decision?

It's really not difficult. Jennifer should choose the course that's in greatest harmony with her current spiritual ideal. If, for now, she decides that her ideal is in greatest agreement with independence, self-growth, and adventure, then the decision is obvious. However, if her spiritual ideal is more compatible with stability, security, and being able to focus on her new job, her decision is also obvious—for now, Jennifer should stay home.

Neither decision was necessarily right; neither was necessarily wrong. However, because of her ideal, Jennifer decided the time had come to move out into her own apartment.

In this example, it would be fair to say that until Jennifer had set/clarified her own spiritual ideal, the decision couldn't have been made comfortably. However, once the spiritual ideal was established, her choice became evident.

Exercise 2.4

You can begin evaluating the decisions you make in any given day in terms of your ideal. Each night before retiring, make a list—not just mentally, but on paper—of your *experiences* that day: list all the decisions that you made and what motivated you to make them. For example, when you decided to fill in as a substitute in the kids' carpool or to help with the dishes, when you decided not to read further in the paper or to call in sick to work, etc.—whatever the decision— note it and then put next to it the motivation on which that decision was based—or as near as you can name it. Why did you decide to do or not do something? It may have been out of laziness or out of service. This will allow you to see whether the spiritual ideal you've chosen has become integrated into your daily life and, if so, how well. The exercise will also allow you to see which areas of your life may need extra work.

You can use the chart below to get started on your journal (It might be a good idea to keep a spiral notebook for an extended period of time):

DECISION	MOTIVATION FOR MAKING THIS DECISION
Example:	
DAY	(i.e., "Who's driving my vehicle?")
Not to clean my room	*Laziness*
DAY ONE	_____
_____	_____
_____	_____
_____	_____

DECISION	MOTIVATION FOR MAKING THIS DECISION
DAY TWO	_____
_____	_____
_____	_____
DAY THREE	_____
_____	_____
_____	_____
DAY FOUR	_____
_____	_____
_____	_____
DAY FIVE	_____
_____	_____
_____	_____
_____	_____

DECISION	MOTIVATION FOR MAKING THIS DECISION
DAY SIX	_____
_____	_____
_____	_____
_____	_____
DAY SEVEN	_____
_____	_____
_____	_____
_____	_____

Although there is space for only seven days here, it is a good idea to keep this journal of your decisions for thirty days. This will allow you to see your progress in working with your ideal over time. At the end of thirty days, note what's happened. You should be able to see some real differences in what you are thinking and what you are thinking about, what your desires are, and what your experiences are.

You don't have to wait seven days (or thirty!) to proceed with the workbook—go at your own pace—but don't neglect completing this exercise either.

A Look in the Rear-View Mirror

As you travel through life, you are always working with an ideal. The key to personal transformation is to become aware of what "motives" have been driving "your car" and then deciding upon a more appropriate "driver" for the direction you wish to take. Your ideal will become a living and dynamic standard by which you measure your daily thoughts and activities. This ideal will be responsible for the way you handle every experience in your life.

You can completely transform the scenery around you by consciously deciding to change what you're viewing—by taking a new and, perhaps, more appropriate route.

In this Second Step you've had a chance to see more clearly where you want to be headed in life and some preliminary things you can do in order to get there. You've also identified a problem relationship that you'd like to work with and established your own personal road map for the major areas of your life.

To conclude this Step, complete the following sentence:

I think I now know where I want to be headed, and one of the essential things I need to do in order to get there is to

_____

_____

_____

_____

And, we'll proceed down the road . . .

STEP THREE:
Watching for Landmarks Along the Way

Once you've decided about the direction you wish to take, the next step involves keeping your eyes open for signs and indicators that verify your course. Every journey you take will have landmarks that can affirm you're headed in the right direction.

Once your ideal has been set, you'll want to establish these signposts or goals in order to check your own progress. As an analogy, when you're on an extended trip traveling along a highway, your progress may appear quite slow even though your car is constantly in motion. In fact, although the landscape may not vary for long stretches of time, you're still moving. If you look carefully, you may even be able to see subtle changes in your surroundings. Eventually, you will also see landmarks (signs, buildings, or scenery) verifying that you're on track. As you realize progress is being made, you may come to feel that—before too long—you'll be able to catch a glimpse of your destination.

By having some of these "landmarks" in mind ahead of time, you'll have an idea of how well you're doing on the journey; you'll know when you've finally arrived at your destination; and you'll have the opportunity to map out a "next trip" with a more challenging destination in mind. In other words, once you've chosen your ideal, it really will be possible to discern whether or not your actions, your thoughts, and your smaller motivational influences are keeping you headed in the right direction.

Exercise 3.1

Before going on a vacation, you may have flipped through a travel brochure and looked at all the sights you'd have the opportunity to see once you arrived at your destination. In fact, even though you had never made the trip before, you probably had some idea of what your chosen destination would be like. Having an idea of where you're going in life and imagining what it may be like once you get there are just as possible.

With that in mind, the purpose of this exercise is to give you an opportunity to view your "perfect day." It's similar to the exercise you completed in Step Two when you imagined a perfect relationship. Once you've established what a perfect day would be like, you might even realize certain steps you can take right now in order to bring this perfect day closer to the present.

For a few moments, close your eyes and think about every possible detail of your perfect day. Since it may take some time for this type of a day to become a reality in your life, *imagine that this day takes place three years in the future.* Think about every item that goes into making the day complete. You may wish to consider everything—from where you're working and what you're doing, to where you're living, who your friends are, how you spend your free time, and even what time you get up in the morning. When you've thought about this day for a few minutes, attempt to answer the following questions: (Remember, don't begin this exercise until you've actually done the "imagination work.")

Does this day involve other people? Family? Business associates? Friends? If so, who are they?

_____

_____

_____

What kinds of activities take place in the course of your perfect day? For example, do you make time for spiritual interests? Mental pursuits? Physical activities?

Spiritual interests: _____

_____

_____

Mental pursuits: _____

_____

_____

Physical activities: _____

_____

_____

In this perfect day, describe where you are and how you spend most of your time:

_____

_____

_____

_____

_____

What makes this "perfect day" three years in the future feel so different from the "everyday days" that you currently experience?

_____

_____

_____

_____

Is there anything you can do in your life to start bringing a portion of this perfect day into your experience right now? Tomorrow? Next week or next month?

_____

_____

_____

_____

Write one thing you're going to begin doing in order to bring this perfect day closer to reality:

_____

_____

_____

_____

Now take a few moments to evaluate the feelings and sensations that were a part of your imagination experience. Using the following key, decide how important each of the factors were in making up your perfect day. You can use as many "4's," "2's," or even "5's," etc., that you want, but take your time.

5 = An Extremely Important Factor
4 = A Somewhat Important Factor
3 = Undecided/Unclear
2 = Not a Very Important Factor
1 = Never a Factor

	5	4	3	2	1
1. FREEDOM	5	4	3	2	1
2. SECURITY	5	4	3	2	1
3. PURPOSEFULNESS	5	4	3	2	1
4. ENJOYMENT	5	4	3	2	1
5. RELAXATION	5	4	3	2	1
6. HUMOR	5	4	3	2	1
7. LOVING ENVIRONMENT	5	4	3	2	1
8. PEACEFUL SURROUNDINGS	5	4	3	2	1
9. PERFECT WEATHER	5	4	3	2	1
10. CREATIVITY	5	4	3	2	1
11. SUPPORTIVE FRIENDS/ FAMILY	5	4	3	2	1
12. JOY IN LIVING	5	4	3	2	1
13. COOPERATION	5	4	3	2	1
14. OTHER:_____	5	4	3	2	1

When you've finished rating the factors, re-read your list and determine if there's a central theme, word, or phrase that best describes your perfect day.

For example, if the most memorable factors for you were purposefulness, enjoyment, humor, and joy in living, then perhaps the word that best describes your day is "Joyfulness." If, on the other hand, your list contains freedom, security, relaxation, and peaceful surroundings as key components, then perhaps the best descriptive word is "Serenity." You might also wish to combine some of your key words into a sentence; for the "joyfulness" example, your sentence might be: "A day where I seem to be really enjoying life and have a definite sense of purpose about what I'm doing."

When you've decided upon the central component(s) of your perfect day, write that descriptive word or phrase here:

_____

_____

_____

_____

_____

_____

_____

Since you've now established the "perfect day" that you'd like to experience in three years, you may wish to refer to this exercise at some point in the future after having worked with ideals for a while (two months? six months? a year?). You might wish to consider some of the events of this day or some of the feelings that you experienced, as the landmarks you'll be looking for along the way that will help to indicate how much progress you're making. Then, when you refer to this exercise, you'll see that your perfect day may be even closer than you thought.

From Exercise 3.1, you've seen some of the important activities and events that would constitute your personal "perfect day." In Step Two you chose a particular ideal as your road map for a relationship, an activity, or a direction in your life. Throughout the rest of Step Three you'll see how the awareness of where it is you want to be headed and the ideal of who it is you want to become are closely connected.

Exercise 3.2

How often have you been driving along toward a familiar destination, such as work or the shopping mall, and found yourself paying very little attention to where you were going or how many others were on the same street, and then before you knew it you had arrived? You found yourself at your destination but had no recall of the actual trip that had taken place. Whenever you're caught up in the spur-of-the-moment hassles or regular day-to-day activities, it's very easy to lose sight of the awareness of where you are and where you're headed.

With this in mind, the following questions will help you step back and take a more detached look at yourself and your interactions with other people. Feel free to answer these questions in your head or on paper, but answer only those that apply to you:

Question One: What sort of a workplace would your company be if every employee were just like you?

_____

_____

_____

_____

Question Two: What sort of home life would there be if every wife/husband were just like you?

_____

_____

_____

_____

Question Three: What sort of families would there be if every child/parent were just like you?

_____

_____

_____

_____

Question Four: What sort of neighborhoods would there be if every neighbor were just like you?

_____

_____

_____

_____

Question Five: What sort of government would there be if every citizen/voter were just like you?

_____

_____

_____

_____

Question Six: What sort of church would your congregation be if every member were just like you?

_____

_____

_____

_____

Question Seven: What sort of self-worth would individuals have if every person had your self-esteem?

_____

_____

_____

_____

Questions like these can be rather pointed as well as a great vehicle for personal introspection. You might wish to look again at the seven questions and ask yourself, "What's the ideal attitude of an employee? Husband/wife? Individual toward him/herself?" etc., as you go through each one. Once you've established the model answer for each response, *these attitudes and behaviors can act as landmarks or signposts along your journey.* For example, let's say that you decide that the ideal attitude for you as a spouse is to be "a supportive listener." Therefore, whenever you *catch yourself* (as opposed to purposefully behaving in that manner) as being a supportive listener, you'll have your encouraging landmark.

When you work with ideals, you may find that you want to rethink them and fine-tune them from time to time. You will make changes in your personalized road map not only for yourself and for your relationship with specific individuals but also for every activity in your life. Ideals change and grow as you do, and the process of watching for landmarks along the way can not only affirm that you're headed in the right direction but can also verify if the direction you're headed in is really where you wanted to go in the first place.

As you decide to rethink your ideals, you can use Exercise 2.3, "the columned approach to ideals," as often as you wish; just take a clean sheet of paper and label the three columns for yourself. This is the approach you will want to use when rethinking ideals. In the process of simply fine-tuning your ideals, however, an exercise like the following can be used (Note: If this is your first time through the workbook, you will probably want to skip doing this as an exercise right now, and instead read it as information to be used after you've worked with your current ideal for awhile).

Exercise 3.3

A simple example of how you might fine-tune your ideals is as follows:

If one of your ideals is "gentleness of speech," try it across the breakfast table tomorrow. Keep working on your conversation until it either matches the ideal or until you have to change the ideal to something else. Perhaps you'll then decide you really want to change the wording of this ideal to "be friendly." Then, do something about it until you've gotten some sort of result. Be friendly. Later you can erase "be friendly" and "gentleness of speech" and several others you've worked on, and sum up all of them in a new ideal—such as "be kind toward people." (People will be kind in return. Remember the first premise of "like attracts like"?)

If you look closely at this example, you may see that each of these "smaller" ideals—gentleness of speech, being friendly, kindness toward people—all involve interaction with others. As the picture below illustrates, these smaller ideals are like portions of a car with the whole vehicle moving in the direction of improving relationships with other people.

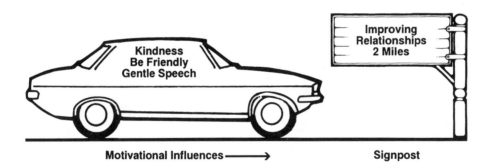

Motivational Influences ⟶   Signpost

The ideal is "Improving Relationships," and each of the motivational influences are helping to move the vehicle toward the final destination. The signpost (or landmark) could be something as simple as seeing a positive reaction in yourself in a situation in which you might normally have experienced difficulty.

As you make certain that each of the motivational influences in your life are driving your vehicle in the same direction, you'll feel like you're making the greatest progress. You will be able to see how your personal application of ideals has altered your perception about your surroundings as well as the people you find in your life. But mostly you'll see how you've helped to foster some real changes within yourself.

Exercise 3.4

The process of spotting signposts serves two purposes as you travel your road map of life. Not only does it give you an idea of where you are going, but it also lets you know where you have been. Parts A and B of this next exercise will let you jot down a few of the signposts or landmarks you'll be looking for as you make your journey.

It might be helpful for you to refer to a couple of previous exercises in order to complete this one. In Exercise 2.1 you had the opportunity to examine a number of qualities that could be used for your ideal (your personal road map). Those qualities were: love, kindness, joy, understanding, patience, gentleness, compassion, humor, faith, trust, commitment, hope, and anything else you might have chosen. In Exercise 1.7 you had the opportunity to examine a frustrating relationship. You may wish to refer to both of these exercises in order to work with parts A and B of the following exercise:

Part A: What am I looking for?

For this portion of the exercise, insert one word or phrase in the blank that will indicate your spiritual ideal. In order for you to see how this exercise flows, an example ("patience") has been inserted inside the parentheses. HOWEVER, INSERT YOUR OWN ROAD MAP WORD OR PHRASE IN THE SPACES PROVIDED AND ANSWER THE QUESTIONS ABOUT *YOUR IDEAL.*

For just a few moments, close your eyes and imagine what a (patient) person would be like. Think about all of the qualities, talents, and traits that would be a part of a (patient) person. When you have a fairly good picture of this type of person in your head, answer the following:

Question One: How does a (patient) —————— person act when dealing with challenging personalities?

_____

_____

_____

Question Two: How does a (patient) _____
person think when confronted with a difficult task or assign-
ment?

_____

_____

_____

Question Three: How does a (patient) _____
person speak to other people who have lost their tempers?

_____

_____

_____

Question Four: What is it about a (patient) _____
person that makes other individuals want to be around that
person?

_____

_____

_____

Question Five: What attitude does a (patient) _____
person have about him/herself?

_____

_____

_____

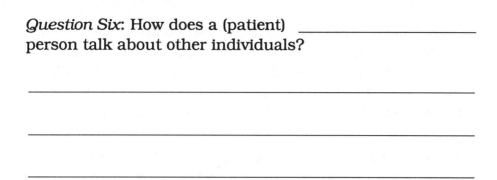

Question Six: How does a (patient) _____
person talk about other individuals?

_____

_____

_____

You might even have additional answers to questions about what (patient) people would be like, how they would think, and how they would act. These answers will assist you in heading in the right direction. The next time you find yourself faced with a challenging individual or a difficult situation or a wearisome decision and you don't want to fall into habitual patterns from the past, stop, fill your ideal in the blank, and ask yourself, "What would a person do in the same situation?" and then act accordingly. You can become the type of person you want to be, in part, by beginning to act like you think that person would behave in the same situation. Your answers to questions like these will also become landmarks and signposts along the way.

Part B: How will I know when I've arrived?

Now that you have some landmarks in mind, how will you know when they've actually been incorporated into your journey? In other words, what kinds of circumstances will let you know the progress that you've made?

These clues may come in many different forms. For example, a major clue might be having an individual with whom you've had a difficult relationship for years *voluntarily* come to you and say something like, "Do you think we could talk about this problem we've had with each other for so long?" Continuing the same example, another significant clue—this time more internal—might be suddenly having a new insight about the individual that totally changes your perception, and consequently your feelings about the person.

On the other hand, a minor clue might be seeming to have more frequent opportunities to "accidentally" run into people or situations with whom or with which you are trying to work. Instead of seeing this as a burden, you'll have the chance to put some of your new-found insights into practice. Oftentimes you'll simply become more aware of a person's whereabouts when you've decided to work on your relationship with him or her.

Other clues are more introspective and have to do with such things as personal journals and dreams. Let's examine how these two tools can be helpful, even if you've never worked with them before.

Exercise 3.5

The last exercise in Section Two suggested that you keep a journal for thirty days. In fact, you're probably still in the midst of that month-long effort. You may wish to begin keeping one for a longer period that includes more than just decisions that you've made. For example, you may wish to write down your thoughts, feelings, and desires, placing special emphasis on a problem situation or a challenging relationship. This journal will allow you to record your progress over time. By reviewing your journal you'll also gain a greater awareness of the problem as a whole. Too often you may find yourself minimizing a challenging situation after a really positive day or exaggerating the same situation after a series of trying experiences.

For simplification, the journal can essentially be seen as a diary of your thoughts, emotions, and actions over a period of time. It might look something like this:

Tuesday, May 8: I had another encounter with Ralph at work today. I thought about my road map, which helped at first, but just thinking about his attitude drives me crazy ...

Friday, May 11: I'm beginning to think this situation with Ralph is hopeless!

Wednesday, May 16: We ran into each other again today, and it was all right ... but I can't help but think he's got something up his sleeve.

Monday, May 21: I was absolutely floored today! Ralph asked me about my weekend ... and he seemed interested in what I had to say. What's up?

Thursday, May 31: Why is it, just when I think there's been a change, he pulls out his personal agenda again! Maybe tomorrow will be better, but today was the pits.

Use the following two pages for getting started on your journal notes. Remember, your notes can be quite simple, but they should focus upon those situations or relationships that you're trying to work with in terms of your personal road map. In the beginning you might wish to have your journal focus upon only one area, such as in the above example about Ralph, but you're welcome to include as many situations or relationships in your notes as you like.

You may not need to make notes every day, simply whenever a situation occurs that is applicable:

Date: _____ Notation One: _____

_____

_____

_____

Date: _____ Notation Two: _____

_____

_____

_____

Date: _____ Notation Three: _____

_____

_____

_____

Date: _____ Notation Four: _____

_____

_____

_____

Date: _____ Notation Five: _____

_____

_____

_____

Date: _____ Notation Six: _____

_____

_____

_____

Date: _____ Notation Seven: _____

_____

_____

_____

Date: _____ Notation Eight: _____

_____

_____

_____

When you are making notes in your journal, it will be important to date your notations; remember, you'll be looking for your *overall progress* over time, not necessarily individual good days or bad days that stand out from the rest.

Exercise 3.6

Often one of the first places you'll see evidence of personal growth is in your dreams. In fact, dreams can provide a rich source of guidance and creative decision making.

For most individuals, the greatest challenge when working with dreams is simply the frustration of interpreting them. However, there are two thoughts that you should keep in mind: (1) Dreams can be extremely helpful even if you don't immediately understand what they mean; and (2) The only way to interpret your dreams is with practice, practice, and more practice.

Therefore, the most important step in working with your dreams is to *write them down*. Keep a pad of paper and a pencil on your nightstand and *first thing* in the morning write down what you remember. It might be only a color or a feeling or a face, or it might be an entire dream. Simply begin to keep track of whatever you remember from your dreams; in time, you'll find the information quite helpful.

A number of excellent books are available on the subject of working with dreams, but perhaps the most beneficial is simply a regular dictionary. Not a dream dictionary, but a *regular dictionary*! Whenever you dream of a symbol that you don't understand, simply look up that word in your dictionary and see whether or not some of the definitions might apply to your particular dream. But in the beginning, more important than "interpreting" your dreams will be recording them.

Since the purpose of this exercise is specifically introspective as it relates to your personal ideal, the most valuable approaches you can use in relation to working with dreams are as follows:

1. Write down your dreams each day.

2. Realize that the *feeling* you had about a dream is at least as important (if not more important) than trying to come up with one definitive interpretation.

78

3. Watch actions, feelings, attitudes, and emotions in your dreams and measure these "subconscious responses" against your conscious waking ideal. For the most part, every character in a dream represents a part of yourself (not simply the character you seem to be in the dream), and these characters can indicate how parts of you are responding to your conscious road map.

For example, dreaming of a "shifty character" who is spying upon the very person with whom you're trying to improve a relationship may simply indicate that there's a part of you who is very wary (perhaps even suspicious) of trying to make the relationship work.

4. Watch for recurring characters, situations, and circumstances in your dreams and note how these characters and situations change over time as you continue to work with your ideal. Positive changes in your waking life are often indicated in dream imagery, whereas "negative" dream imagery might simply be pointing out stubborn areas in your life.

5. Remember the two most important factors (cited above) when working with dreams: (1) Dreams can be extremely helpful even if you don't immediately understand what they mean; and (2) The only way to interpret your dreams is with practice, practice, and more practice.

The following pages are for you to get started on your dream notebook; this process is similar to keeping a journal, so you may wish to begin a separate spiral notebook as well:

Date: _____ Dream: _____

_____

_____

_____

Date: _____ Dream: _____

_____

_____

_____

Date: _____ Dream: _____

_____

_____

_____

Date: _____ Dream: _____

_____

_____

_____

Date: _____ Dream: _____

_____

_____

_____

Date: _____ Dream: _____

_____

_____

_____

Date: _____ Dream: _____

_____

_____

_____

Date: _____ Dream: _____

_____

_____

_____

As you work with introspective tools such as dreams and journaling, you'll begin to have exciting insights (and positive feedback!) about your life. These insights are some of the landmarks and signposts you can discover within yourself. With just a few minutes invested each day, in time you'll become a "professional" journaler and dreamer and in the process discover a rich source of guidance that you had within you all along.

A Look in the Rear-View Mirror:

The road connecting where you are right now and the place where you want to be is simply representative of doing what you know to do one step at a time. In becoming consistent with your application—by taking out your road map and getting a bearing from time to time—you'll be able to see some real changes. Certainly, the first changes you'll discover are within yourself, but, as you begin to change, the people around you will "miraculously" change as well.

If, as you travel life's highways, you find that you're not satisfied with your direction, don't feel sorry or angry that you've chosen the wrong road . . . just turn around! Ideals change as you do, but what is most important is that ideals grow over time.

Perhaps the easiest way to find your bearings is to take note of the landmarks and signposts along the way. Not only can they confirm your direction, but they can also assure you that you're going where you want to be.

To conclude this Step, complete the following sentence:

Perhaps one of the greatest "signposts" I could see within myself to verify that I'm making progress is

_____

_____

_____

And, we'll proceed down the road . . .

STEP FOUR:
Your Definitive Journey

For most individuals, the very first experience of driving a car probably lasted just a short length of time—perhaps your mother or father let you back the family car out of the driveway, or maybe you were allowed to drive a little ways down a deserted road for practice. It would be a very long while before you had the nerve or even the ability to take the car out for an extended period. However, as time went on you became braver and more confident behind the wheel and the journeys you were comfortable with became longer. In a similar vein, when you were a young child, the height you hoped to reach was probably lower than the height you hoped to attain as a teenager. Your sights were raised as you yourself grew. Your own road map, your ideal, will be affected in the same way by personal growth and experience.

Where Am I Going?

From a practical perspective, everyone wants to be headed toward the same destination: "better" relationships, "better" opportunities, a "better" life in general. Interestingly enough, from a "spiritual" point of view, everyone is also headed toward the same destination although—as the following illustrates—the directions they appear to be taking might seem quite different. [For ease of illustration, let's call that destination "Understanding the Purpose of Life," or "Being More Spiritual," or "Having a Relationship with God"]:

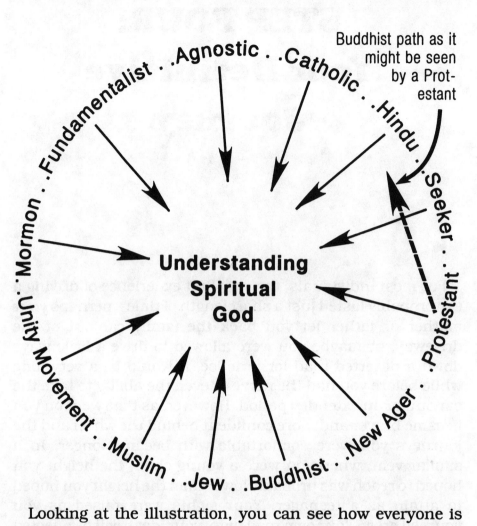

Looking at the illustration, you can see how everyone is headed toward the same destination (or the same ideal), even though the directions being taken might appear quite different. For ease of explanation, let's say that a Protestant's ideal is taking him or her in a direction that appears westward in the illustration (unbroken line). Note the result if, for example, a Buddhist tried to explain to a Protestant his or her own path, which appears to be northwesterly in the diagram (broken line). To the Protestant it might appear as though the Buddhist's path wasn't going in the right direction at all.

In practical terms, what this picture illustrates is the fact that, although your ideal may be identical to someone else's, your ideas of how to get there and your goals for making the journey are always going to be your own.

Exercise 4.1

Thus far, you have seen how consciously setting a road map can give you a focus for your life's direction. It is the method by which you became aware of all your motivational influences, making certain that they are headed in the same direction. You've seen how journaling can be helpful for "logging" each step of your journey—small steps that might otherwise be overlooked. You also had the opportunity to begin thinking about (and recording!) your dreams—by doing so, you saw how your subconscious mind can provide another perspective on the thoughts, feelings, and actions of everyday life. In addition to these tools, the regular practice of meditation can be invaluable for focusing your awareness and becoming the navigator of every motivational influence in your life.

Research has long verified the effectiveness of meditation; it's no longer thought of it as just some kind of a "fad." In fact, meditation has been found to help reduce anxiety, assist in lowering blood pressure, and facilitate physiological well-being. From the perspective of ideals, meditation is invaluable at focusing your conscious mind and thereby coordinating all your thoughts so that they become more in alignment with your personal road map.

The steps to meditation are simple. So simple, in fact, that even a beginner can start to feel the positive effects of this relaxation technique from the very first:

Step One: Have a regular time and place for your 10- to 15-minute meditation session. Be certain to choose a time when you are most likely to be alert and least likely to be distracted.

Step Two: Get physically comfortable. You may wish to be seated in a cozy chair or on your bed, but sit in a place where you can keep your spine comfortably straight. Begin to relax—imagining that you are breathing in relaxation and breathing out any anxiety or stress. Do this for a good three to five minutes, however long it takes for you to begin to feel comfortable and at ease.

Step Three: Now focus your mind on your ideal or a longer phrase (also called an affirmation) that contains the feeling of your ideal. Instead of your trying to have a "blank mind" and sitting quietly, true meditation involves focusing upon a single, calming thought. For example, if the road map you're currently following is "Love," then "Love" could be the focus of your meditation period. A longer affirmation containing the same ideal might be something like: "The love of God fills my being."

With this word or phrase in your mind, repeat it slowly to yourself.

Step Four: The first "stage" of meditation involves thinking about the message of your affirmation. In the example from Step Three, you would think about the message of "The love of God fills my being." After a few moments the second "stage" occurs, which consists of the *feeling* evoked by your affirmation. Keeping your mind focused upon the feeling is what true meditation is all about. As an analogy, you can say the words "I love my child" and there is real meaning behind those words. However, the *feeling* of those words seems much more meaningful than simply the words themselves.

Try to stay focused upon the *feeling* that is evoked inside of you. When your mind wanders, simply bring it back to the words of your affirmation and begin thinking/feeling the meaning once again. In the beginning you may find that your mind wanders more than it stays focused, but with practice the centering will become much easier. For five to ten minutes, continue to focus on "Love" or whatever else you've chosen as your affirmation. Remember, don't worry about your mind wandering; simply bring it back to the feeling of your ideal.

Step Five: At the end of your meditation session, spend a few moments sending out good thoughts or prayers to others. You will have created good feelings (and "vibes") within yourself, and you will want to share these thoughts with others. In fact, you may find this step of your meditation session as important to you as the quiet time.

Step Six: Be consistent. Try to make meditation a regular part of your daily routine—even if it's for just a few moments each day. You'll find that you will "carry" an awareness of your ideal with you throughout the day more readily on those days that you've worked with meditation. In time, you'll discover that meditation is an enjoyable experience—something you look forward to doing, and not just one more thing that has to be done in your already hectic schedule.

For a week, you might wish to briefly record your feelings and relaxation level before and after a 10- to 15-minute meditation session. You can use the following spaces to record any thoughts or sensations that you have:

Meditation, Day One:

Feelings/Relaxation Level (before meditation):

_____

_____

_____

Feelings/Relaxation Level (after meditation):

_____

_____

_____

Meditation, Day Two:

Feelings/Relaxation Level (before meditation):

_____

_____

_____

Feelings/Relaxation Level (after meditation):

_____

_____

_____

Meditation, Day Three:

Feelings/Relaxation Level (before meditation):

_____

_____

_____

Feelings/Relaxation Level (after meditation):

_____

_____

_____

Meditation, Day Four:

Feelings/Relaxation Level (before meditation):

_____

_____

_____

Feelings/Relaxation Level (after meditation):

_____

_____

_____

Meditation, Day Five:

Feelings/Relaxation Level (before meditation):

_____

_____

_____

Feelings/Relaxation Level (after meditation):

_____

_____

_____

Meditation, Day Six:

Feelings/Relaxation Level (before meditation):

_____

_____

_____

Feelings/Relaxation Level (after meditation):

_____

_____

_____

Meditation, Day Seven:

Feelings/Relaxation Level (before meditation):

_____

_____

_____

Feelings/Relaxation Level (after meditation):

_____

_____

_____

With practice, meditation will become easier and the relaxation level you experience will become much more noticeable. But, more important, you may find meditation as the single most important "navigational tool" for staying focused on your road map and your journey through life.

Exercise 4.2

As you begin working with ideals, becoming aware of your direction, improving your relationships with others, and feeling more in control of your life, your ideals will expand and grow. Eventually, they will become the single most important pattern in your life—and, as you grow and change, the pattern you hope to attain will grow and change as well. Until, finally, *your* true ideal will reflect the highest spiritual attainment that you can imagine *anyone ever* reaching.

In fact, you can often catch glimpses of your own "ultimate destination" in other people, such as spiritual leaders, historical figures, or even Biblical characters that you respect or admire. To be ideal patterns, these individuals should exhibit human potential at its highest as well as advocate service to others. In other words, it is as important to have compassion for the individuals you find traveling life's highways as it is to take responsibility for your own journey. These ultimate patterns are figures who have often "taken their own wheel" and worked with ideals, such as forgiveness, love, compassion, humanitarianism, etc.

Examples of individuals whom you might wish to emulate in your own life may be the following: Jesus, Buddha, Mohammed, Abraham, Mother Teresa, Moses, a particular saint, a revered rabbi, or whomever you personally consider to be the "ultimate example" of an ideal life. You could also decide, instead, to pick a word or set of words, such as "Unconditional Love" or "Oneness," as a pattern to emulate. *It is not important what the words or names mean to someone else. It only matters that what you choose awakens within you an awareness of the very highest you could possibly imagine.*

In the following space, please write the name or word(s) that awakens within you the ultimate example of how an individual could live his or her life:

_____

Close your eyes for just a moment and try to imagine this person (or, if you've chosen a word, a person that exemplifies this characteristic). Imagine that this person is standing before you. Think about his or her qualities, talents, and traits. When you have the person's qualities in mind, make a list of them in the left-hand column. For each one, try to decide exactly what it is about that quality that appeals to you, making notes in the right-hand column [don't forget to do your "imagination work" first]:

QUALITY	ADMIRABLE BECAUSE
Example:	
Unconditional love	*Would make me feel totally accepted for who I am*

You might say that your personal attainment of each of these qualities could become "steps" toward your becoming more and more like the individual whom you regard as the ultimate example. In fact, the list of characteristics for this "ideal person" might look very much like the list referred to in Exercise 2.1: Love, Kindness, Joy, Understanding, Patience, Gentleness, Compassion, Forgiveness, Humor, Faith, Trust, Commitment, and Hope. What's different about this exercise, however, is that each of these ingredients are elements of a larger ideal, whereas in Exercise 2.1 the individual qualities were ideals themselves. Remember, ideals will grow and expand as you do.

From a *strictly psychological* perspective, the reason that certain spiritual figures evoke a special reverence and feeling of appreciation inside you is because they act as "archetypes" (or patterns) for goodness. In other words, the subconscious mind sees these figures as examples of human spirituality, and the mind recognizes the existence of these very same patterns within yourself—even if they are currently dormant! In fact, these patterns have been called the "awareness within each soul of the soul's oneness with God."

For now, you will probably want to choose to work with a road map that contains "smaller ideals," instead of choosing one of these ultimate examples just yet. You won't want to pick the "unreachable" anytime soon; instead, you need shorter-range ideals as goals so that you can experience real progress, reward yourself, and then choose your "next step." It's similar to the process of "fine-tuning" your ideals, as mentioned in Exercise 3.3. However, from this exercise you've got an idea of the final destination toward which you'll be heading.

Using the previous car illustration, you might look at your ultimate destination as something like this:

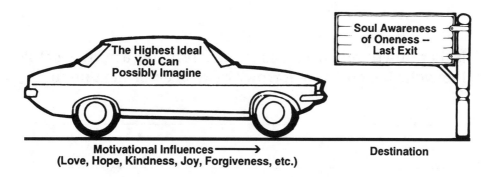

Exercise 4.3

The time has come for you to decide again what is your greatest joy? What is it you want, more than anything, out of life? Who do you want to become? For a few moments, close your eyes and think about the answers to these questions. First, do your "imaging"; perhaps you'd even like to have a brief meditation first and afterwards reflect on these questions. Then, respond to the following:

Is there anything you really want to do (regardless of your current perception of your potential) . . . the sky is the limit! What is it your soul longs to do?

_____

_____

_____

_____

Is there anything you can do to begin bringing a portion of this into your life now? Tomorrow? Next week or next month?

_____

_____

_____

_____

_____

Is there any "excess baggage" that you'll need to get rid of (perhaps old habitual patterns, or discouraging thoughts, or too many opposing desires and motivational influences)? If so, what are they?

_____

_____

_____

_____

Is there anything you can begin doing now to get rid of this excess baggage? How about tomorrow? Next week or next month?

_____

_____

_____

_____

Finally, if at death you had the opportunity to review your life, then:

1) What *quality* would you like others to attribute to you?

_____

_____

_____

_____

2) What relationships would you like to look back on as being "healed"?

_____

_____

_____

_____

3) What relationships would you like to remember most fondly?

_____

_____

_____

_____

A Look in the Rear-View Mirror

Life is an adventure, and it is filled with experiences, choices, and opportunities. This adventure is your personal journey—a journey in which you have the right to control much of your experience. You have the free will to decide where you want to go, the path you want to follow, and the feelings and attitudes you wish to adopt along the way.

By simply gaining an awareness of how your decisions affect your experience, you can begin to make conscious choices corresponding to a proper motivation and, in turn, alter your perceptions and your experiences. Your ideal is the key to setting everything in motion.

To conclude this step, complete the following sentence:

More than anything else, I'm looking forward to the next stage of my journey through life because

_____

_____

_____

_____

Therefore, put your key in the ignition, take the wheel, get ready with your road map. You are now in the driver's seat, so proceed down the road!

Suggestions for Using Your Workbook

After completing the exercises outlined in this workbook, you will want to refer to this material from time to time. The author's suggestions are as follows:

1) You will probably want to refer to and work with Exercises 2.3 and 3.3 more frequently than some of the others, creating your road map and fine-tuning it as you travel life's highways.

2) Your introspective work with journaling, or dreams, or meditation, or a combination of each of them, should become important ingredients in your life's course.

3) As problem relationships or people arise in your life, working with Exercise 2.2 (in addition to introspective work) will probably give you the greatest assistance.

4) It will be fun, from time to time, to review and catch a glimpse of your "perfect day." For this reason, you may wish to redo Exercise 3.1 every three to six months.

5) Finally, you may wish to take some clean sheets of paper and rework all of your Ideals Workbook periodically at some point in the future. In fact, eventually you may wish to do something like this annually, perhaps in conjunction with a "New Year" and the setting of resolutions.

Happy traveling!

The most important experience for any individual is to first know what is the ideal. Based on Edgar Cayce reading 357-13

THOUGHTS ON MY IDEALS:

THOUGHTS ON MY IDEALS:

_____

THOUGHTS ON MY IDEALS:

What Is A.R.E.?

The Association for Research and Enlightenment, Inc. (A.R.E.®), is the international headquarters for the work of Edgar Cayce (1877-1945), who is considered the best-documented psychic of the twentieth century. Founded in 1931, the A.R.E. consists of a community of people from all walks of life and spiritual traditions, who have found meaningful and life-transformative insights from the readings of Edgar Cayce.

Although A.R.E. headquarters is located in Virginia Beach, Virginia— where visitors are always welcome—the A.R.E. community is a global network of individuals who offer conferences, educational activities, and fellowship around the world. People of every age are invited to participate in programs that focus on such topics as holistic health, dreams, reincarnation, ESP, the power of the mind, meditation, and personal spirituality.

In addition to study groups and various activities, the A.R.E. offers membership benefits and services, a bimonthly magazine, a newsletter, extracts from the Cayce readings, conferences, international tours, a massage school curriculum, an impressive volunteer network, a retreat-type camp for children and adults, and A.R.E. contacts around the world. A.R.E. also maintains an affiliation with Atlantic University, which offers a master's degree program in Transpersonal Studies.

For additional information about A.R.E. activities hosted near you, please contact:

A.R.E.
67th St. and Atlantic Ave.
P.O. Box 595
Virginia Beach, VA 23451-0595
(804) 428-3588

A.R.E. Press

A.R.E. Press is a publisher and distributor of books, audiotapes, and videos that offer guidance for a more fulfilling life. Our products are based on, or are compatible with, the concepts in the psychic readings of Edgar Cayce.

For a free catalog, please write to A.R.E. Press at the address below or call toll free 1-800-723-1112. For any other information, please call 804-428-3588.

A.R.E. Press
Sixty-Eighth & Atlantic Avenue
P.O. Box 656
Virginia Beach, VA 23451-0656